Hello!

Thank you so much for buying this journal! Inside you'll find a place to release all of your thoughts. Doodle, color, create!

Start making it yours by writing your name below!

NAME:

_ _

CONTENTS

ONE
CREATE YOUR OWN AFFIRMATIONS

Create Your Own Affirmations

Write 5 (or more) self affirmations (ex. I am beautiful)

Remember you don't have to believe the affirmations yet. Writing them helps lead to self-love and acceptance!

Create Your Own Affirmations

Write 5 (or more) self affirmations (ex. I am beautiful)

Remember you don't have to believe the affirmations yet. Writing them helps lead to self-love and acceptance!

Create Your Own Affirmations

Write 5 (or more) self affirmations (ex. I am beautiful)

Remember you don't have to believe the affirmations yet. Writing them helps lead to self-love and acceptance!

Create Your Own Affirmations

Write 5 (or more) self affirmations (ex. I am beautiful)

Remember you don't have to believe the affirmations yet. Writing them helps lead to self-love and acceptance!

TWO

SELF-CARE Q&A

Self-Care Q&A

ANSWER HONESTLY!

How do I feel today?

_____

When was the last time I showered?

_____

What self-affirming activities have I been practicing?

_____

Am I recieving the care I need?

_____

What type of support do I need? From who?

_____

What can I do right now to improve my situation?

_____

Self-Care Q&A

ANSWER HONESTLY!

How do I feel today?

_____

When was the last time I showered?

_____

What self-affirming activities have I been practicing?

_____

Am I recieving the care I need?

_____

What type of support do I need? From who?

_____

What can I do right now to improve my situation?

_____

Self-Care Q&A

ANSWER HONESTLY!

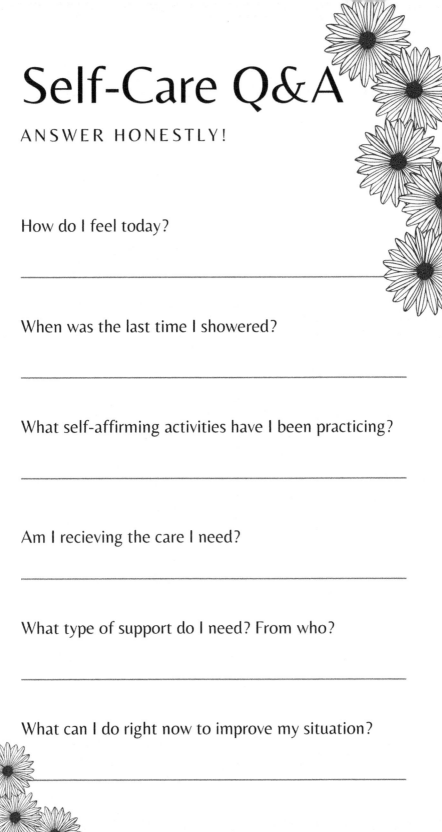

How do I feel today?

_____

When was the last time I showered?

_____

What self-affirming activities have I been practicing?

_____

Am I recieving the care I need?

_____

What type of support do I need? From who?

_____

What can I do right now to improve my situation?

_____

self-care checklist

CHECK THE BOXES OF THE ACTIVITIES
YOUVE COMPLETED

- ☐ TAKEN A SHOWER
- ☐ BRUSHED YOUR TEETH
- ☐ DONE A FACE OR HAIR MASK
- ☐ SPENT 5+ MINUTES CLEANING
- ☐ LISTENED TO YOUR FAVORITE SONG
- ☐ EXCERCISED
- ☐ TALKED TO SOMEONE YOU LOVE
- ☐ SPENT TIME OUTSIDE
- ☐ MANICURE/PEDICURE
- ☐ CUDDLED A STUFFED ANIMAL
- ☐ WATCHED TV OR A MOVIE
- ☐ EATEN SOMETHING
- ☐ READ A BOOK

self-care checklist

**CHECK THE BOXES OF THE ACTIVITIES
YOUVE COMPLETED**

- [ ] TAKEN A SHOWER
- [ ] BRUSHED YOUR TEETH
- [ ] DONE A FACE OR HAIR MASK
- [ ] SPENT 5+ MINUTES CLEANING
- [ ] LISTENED TO YOUR FAVORITE SONG
- [ ] EXCERCISED
- [ ] TALKED TO SOMEONE YOU LOVE
- [ ] SPENT TIME OUTSIDE
- [ ] MANICURE/PEDICURE
- [ ] CUDDLED A STUFFED ANIMAL
- [ ] WATCHED TV OR A MOVIE
- [ ] EATEN SOMETHING
- [ ] READ A BOOK

self-care checklist

**CHECK THE BOXES OF THE ACTIVITIES
YOUVE COMPLETED**

- [ ] TAKEN A SHOWER
- [ ] BRUSHED YOUR TEETH
- [ ] DONE A FACE OR HAIR MASK
- [ ] SPENT 5+ MINUTES CLEANING
- [ ] LISTENED TO YOUR FAVORITE SONG
- [ ] EXCERCISED
- [ ] TALKED TO SOMEONE YOU LOVE
- [ ] SPENT TIME OUTSIDE
- [ ] MANICURE/PEDICURE
- [ ] CUDDLED A STUFFED ANIMAL
- [ ] WATCHED TV OR A MOVIE
- [ ] EATEN SOMETHING
- [ ] READ A BOOK

Self-Care Bingo

TOOK A SHOWER	GOT DRESSED	CAUGHT UP WITH FRIENDS	CRAFT TIME	COMPLIMENTED MYSELF
MEDITATED	ATE SOME FOOD	STRETCHED	HAD FUN	ASKED FOR HELP
KARAOKE	DRANK WATER	*Free*	COLORING TIME	FACE MASK TIME
DANCE PARTY	TOOK A NAP	BAKED SOMETHING	HUGGED A STUFFED ANIMAL	WATCHED MY FAV TV SHOW
TOOK A MENTAL HEALTH DAY	SPENT TIME OUTSIDE	CLEANED MY ROOM	SPENT TIME JOURNALING	SAID I LOVE MYSELF

Self-Care Bingo

TOOK A SHOWER	GOT DRESSED	CAUGHT UP WITH FRIENDS	CRAFT TIME	COMPLIMENTED MYSELF
MEDITATED	ATE SOME FOOD	STRETCHED	HAD FUN	ASKED FOR HELP
KARAOKE	DRANK WATER	*Free*	COLORING TIME	FACE MASK TIME
DANCE PARTY	TOOK A NAP	BAKED SOMETHING	HUGGED A STUFFED ANIMAL	WATCHED MY FAV TV SHOW
TOOK A MENTAL HEALTH DAY	SPENT TIME OUTSIDE	CLEANED MY ROOM	SPENT TIME JOURNALING	SAID I LOVE MYSELF

CHOCOLATE MUG CAKE

A quick sweet treat

INGREDIENTS

- 3 tablespoons flour
- 3 tablespoons cocoa powder
- 3 tablespoons sugar
- a pinch of salt
- a pinch of baking powder
- 3 tablespoons milk
- 2 tablespoons vegetable oil
- chocolate chips (optional)
- a little bit of vanilla extract (I'm talking a splash plz do not put a lot in)

PREP TIME

- Prep | 5 m
- Cook | 90 sec

PROCEDURE

01 Mix flour, sugar, cocoa powder and baking powder together in the mug.

02 Mix milk, oil, and vanilla extract in with the dry ingredients. Add chocolate chips if you want. I'm not teling you what to do.

03 Put the mug in the microwave for 90 seconds. Don't over cook it or your mug cake will be dry. And that'll be less than desirable.

04 Personally I like to add extra butter and sugar on top or whipped cream. Now you're all done! Eat the mug cake. Or give it to a friend. Just make sure someone eats it.

THREE
MINDFULNESS

Mindfulness

Take a moment to be observant and mindful.

Close your eyes. What do you smell? What do you hear?
How does the floor feel beneath you?
Write a piece about your current environment as
if you were explaining it to an alien.

Mindfulness

Take a moment to be observant and mindful.

How is the weather today? Is it the perfect day to drink a warm cup of coffee or would an ice cold watermelon shake be more ideal? Write a piece about your current location's weather situation and the ideal activities for it.

JOURNAL MOMENT

MUSIC & LYRICS

If you had to choose any song to be your theme song, what is it and why? Copy down some of the lyrics and why they are meaningful.

JOURNAL MOMENT

Pick a person you'd love to interview. Next, think of questions you'd ask.
Now answer those questions how you think the person would respond.

JOURNAL MOMENT

SMELLS LIKE...

Describe your favorite smells. How do they make you feel? What do they remind you of?

As Black women our strength is legendary.

But remember, there is strength in vulnerability.

You deserve to be cherished.
You deserve care.
You deserve protection.

Never let anyone use your strength
as an excuse to deny your humanity.

As a free Black girl you have the right to be wonderfully
flawed,
emotionally dynamic
and fully you.

Terreece M. Clarke,

GLOW UP
WORD SEARCH

L	I	Z	U	E	E	B	T	D	T	A	B	U	I
L	E	A	F	S	C	R	F	A	C	I	R	H	R
E	Y	A	A	B	A	A	I	Z	D	R	I	A	C
E	O	L	U	I	E	V	E	Z	I	I	L	P	A
I	J	A	E	S	P	E	R	L	V	B	L	P	E
S	U	P	E	R	B	Z	C	I	I	G	I	Y	X
G	N	I	W	O	L	G	E	N	N	E	A	L	Q
B	E	A	M	I	N	G	N	G	E	P	N	U	U
I	W	O	N	D	R	O	U	S	R	O	T	M	I
I	E	E	R	A	C	F	L	E	S	H	I	I	S
E	O	S	U	O	I	R	O	T	C	I	V	N	I
I	E	M	A	V	G	N	I	L	A	E	H	O	T
B	L	S	L	U	F	I	T	U	A	E	B	U	E
I	T	A	M	A	Z	I	N	G	F	R	I	S	S

LUMINOUS
DAZZLING
BEAMING
DIVINE
BRILLIANT
HOPE
GLOWING
WONDROUS
EXQUISITE
FIERCE
VICTORIOUS
SELF CARE
AMAZING
HEALING
BEAUTIFUL
PEACE
SUPERB
HAPPY
JOY
BRAVE

What's upsetting you?

What do you hate? What is bothering you? Write it here and then destroy this page.
Rip it up. Burn it. Crumple it. Whatever you need.

What's upsetting you?

What do you hate? What is bothering you? Write it here and then destroy this page.
Rip it up. Burn it. Crumple it. Whatever you need.

What's upsetting you?

What do you hate? What is bothering you? Write it here and then destroy this page.
Rip it up. Burn it. Crumple it. Whatever you need.

What's upsetting you?

What do you hate? What is bothering you? Write it here and then destroy this page.
Rip it up. Burn it. Crumple it. Whatever you need.

What's upsetting you?

Write it here and then destroy this page.
Rip it up. Burn it. Crumple it. Whatever you need.

What's upsetting you?

Write it here and then destroy this page.
Rip it up. Burn it. Crumple it. Whatever you need.

FOUR

GRATITUDE!

LIST SOME THINGS THAT YOU LOVE

What makes you happy?

- [ ]
- [ ]
- [ ]
- [ ]
- [ ]
- [ ]
- [ ]
- [ ]
- [ ]
- [ ]
- [ ]
- [ ]

LIST SOME THINGS THAT YOU LOVE

What makes you happy?

☐
☐
☐
☐
☐
☐
☐
☐
☐
☐
☐

LIST SOME THINGS THAT YOU ARE GRATEFUL FOR TODAY

Gratitude

☐
☐
☐
☐
☐
☐
☐
☐
☐
☐
☐
☐
☐

LIST SOME THINGS THAT YOU ARE GRATEFUL FOR TODAY

More Gratitude

- ☐
- ☐
- ☐
- ☐
- ☐
- ☐
- ☐
- ☐
- ☐
- ☐
- ☐
- ☐
- ☐

FIVE THINGS

That Went Well Today...

1.

2.

3.

4.

5.

To survive and thrive you must find
the good in everyday life

That Went Well Today...

1.

2.

3.

4.

5.

To survive and thrive you must find
the good in everyday life

That Went Well
Today...

1.

2.

3.

4.

5.

To survive and thrive you must find
the good in everyday life

Joy Journal

Reflection and Realizations

*There is always something in which you can find joy.
Write about today's joy.*

Joy Journal

Reflection and Realizations

What sounds give you joy? Close your eyes and imagine them... Now write them and let the joy bubble up.

Joy Journal

Reflection and Realizations

What is your favorite color and why does it bring you joy?

Joy Journal

Reflection and Realizations

What at school brings you joy?

Joy Journal

Reflection and Realizations

If you could bottle joy and share it, what ingredients
would go inside? What would the bottle look like?

Joy Journal

Reflection and Realizations

What do you want to remember about today?

Joy Journal

Reflection and Realizations

There is always something in which you can find joy.
Write about today's joy.

FIVE

DRAW YOURSELF

Draw Yourself

*Imagine yourself where you want to be in the future -
then draw it!*

Add a caption

Draw Yourself

• • • • • • • ❖ • • • • • • •

Imagine yourself where you want to be in the future -
then draw it!

Add a caption

SIX

WRITE A LETTER

Write a letter to yourself to encourage yourself!

Dear _____

Write a letter to yourself to encourage yourself!

Dear _____

Write a letter to someone who you need to talk to.

Dear _____

Write a letter to your school.

Dear _____

SEVEN

PICTURE TIME!

TAPE A PICTURE OF YOU
AND YOUR FRIENDS

Remember to hold the ones you love
close to you

EIGHT

FILL IN THE BLANK

Black Hair Magic Edition

YOUR FAVORITE HAIRSTYLE:

I LOVE IT WHEN MY HAIR:

THREE WORDS TO DESCRIBE MY HAIR

I LOVE MY HAIR BECAUSE

TO KEEP MY HAIR HEALTHY I:

BLACK GIRL MAGIC

In the moment...

FILL IN THE BLANKS!

Last thing I ate:

Last person I talked to:

Last song I listed to:

Last movie I watched:

Last book I read:

FINISH THE SENTENCE

EVERY MORNING, I

I CAN'T LEAVE THE HOUSE WITHOUT

MY USUAL BREAKFAST IS

I STUDY/WORK AT

WHEN I GET HOME, I

YOU HAVE A DIVINE
RIGHT TO TAKE UP SPACE

ALL ABOUT ME

GIF CHALLENGE

Me as a GIF

My favorite food

Favorite Daytime
Activity

My Love Language

Dream trip

My music taste

NINE

VENT PAGES

Vent Journal

DATE

Did you have a rough day? Go ahead and vent about it here.

- What happened?
- What did you do?
- What did you wish you had done?
- How can you make the situation better?
- Is it worth spending your time and energy on?
- How are you feeling?

Vent Journal

DATE

Did you have a rough day? Go ahead and vent about it here.

- What happened?
-What did you do?
- What did you wish you had done?
- How can you make the situation better?
- Is it worth spending your time and energy on?
- How are you feeling?

Vent Journal

DATE

Did you have a rough day? Go ahead and vent about it here.

- What happened?
-What did you do?
- What did you wish you had done?
- How can you make the situation better?
- Is it worth spending your time and energy on?
- How are you feeling?

Vent Journal

DATE

Did you have a rough day? Go ahead and vent about it here.

- What happened?
- What did you do?
- What did you wish you had done?
- How can you make the situation better?
- Is it worth spending your time and energy on?
- How are you feeling?

Tap into your sources of power.

There is so much really heavy content everywhere we look — television, social media, even conversations with friends and family can stir up a lot of emotions.

It is critically important to seek out authors, podcasts, youtube videos and other forms of media that speak life into you.
Who are the people or programs that leave you feeling hopeful and inspired?

Flood your mind with those messages and surround yourself with positive people.

Reba Peoples, M.D.

" Yesterday is gone
and tomorrow has yet to reveal itself.

Explore today with wonder
and excitement.

Live fully in each moment
of this day. "

Jocelyn M. Armstrong, Esq.

DOTS PAGE

Connect The Dots
(It's Soothing)

JOURNAL SHEETS

ALSO BY OLIVIA V.G. CLARKE

Black Girl, White School: Thriving, Surviving and No, You Can't Touch My Hair

Black Girl, White School: The Ally Journal

Made in the USA
Middletown, DE
12 October 2020